Say the sounds and blend them together to read the words.

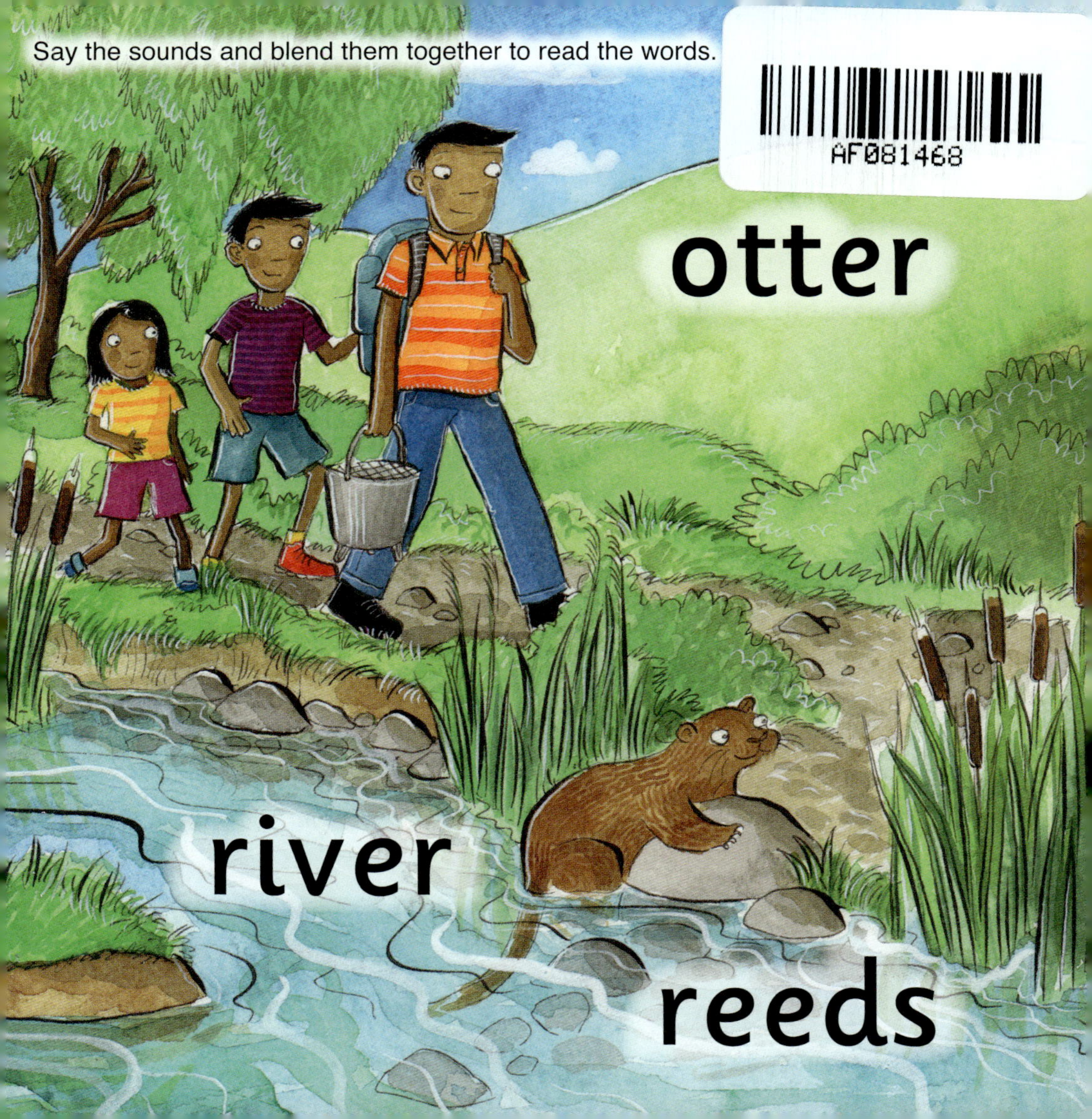

AF081468

kingfisher

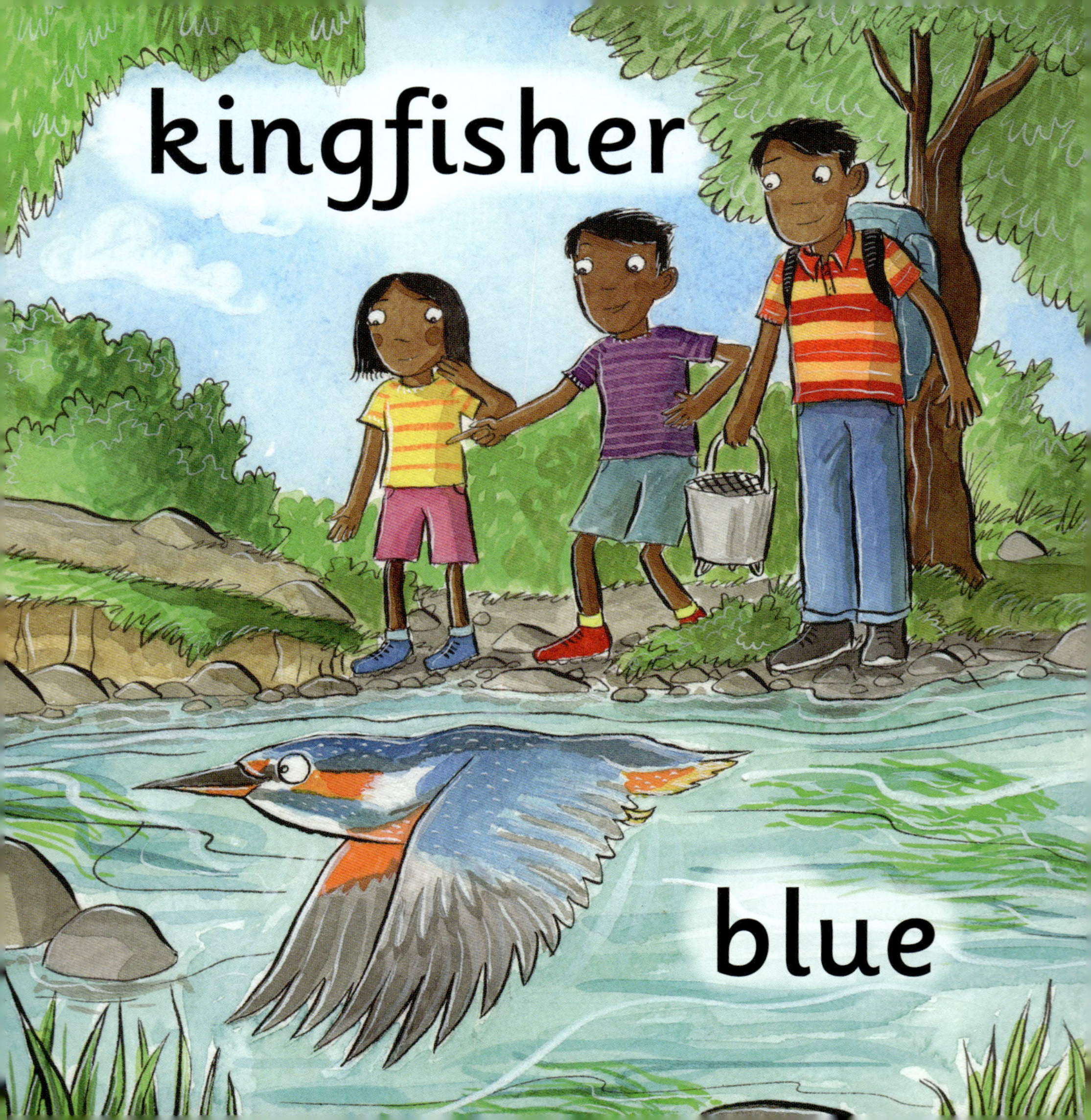

blue

Say the word *twig* and listen out for the sounds: *twig* – /t-w-i-g/. (There is one sound dot underneath the twig for each sound in the word.)

rock

dragonflies

tree
quack

Look at the letters and say the sounds. See how quickly you can say all of them.

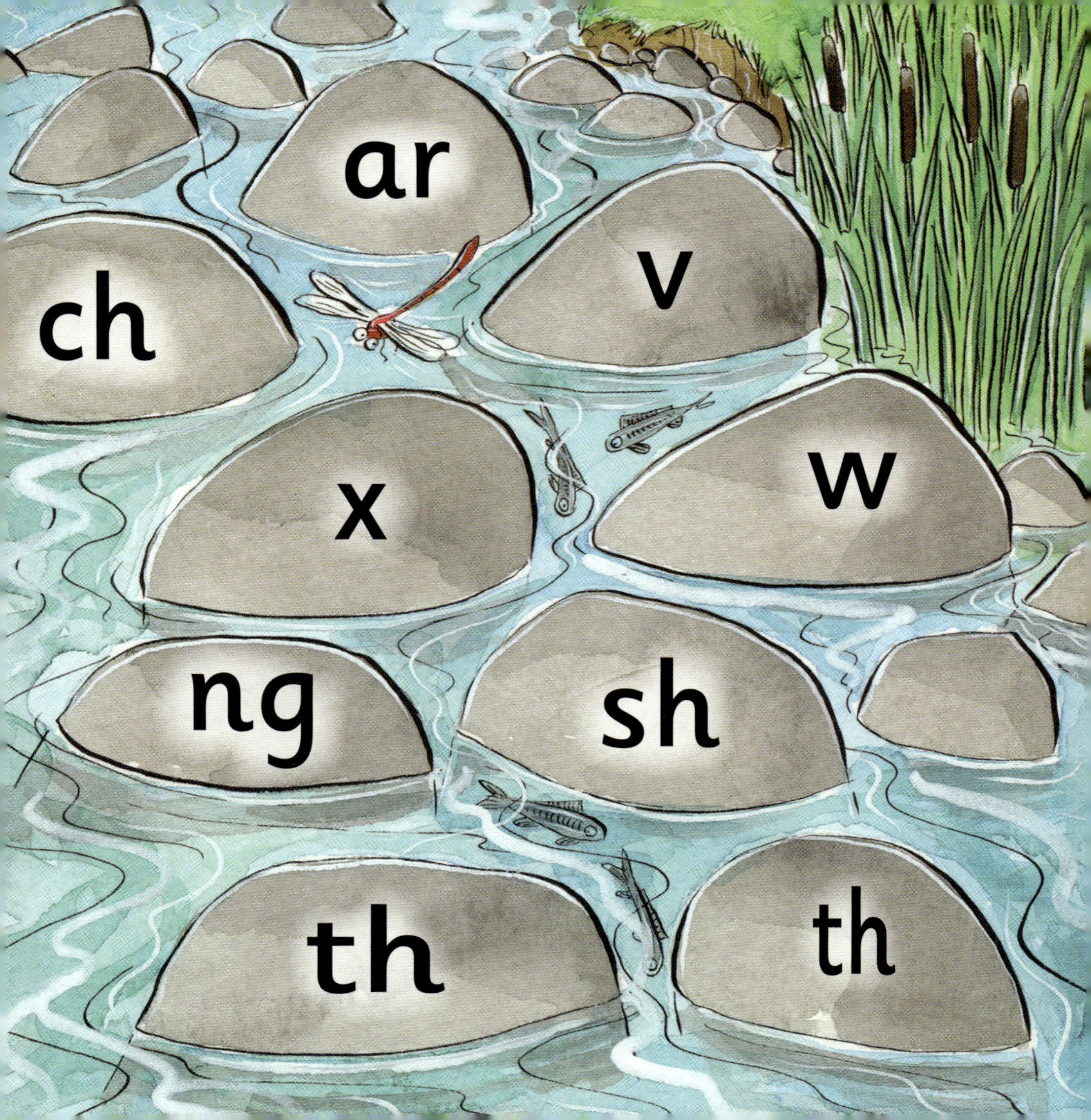
ar
ch
v
x
w
ng
sh
th
th

fisherman

shout

Letters in faint type are silent letters and do not make a sound in the word.

perch

trout

barbecue